# WILL
# SELF

---

# HOW
# WAS
# YOUR
# DAY?

How Was Your Day?
Will Self

ISBN  978-1-903110-52-2

First published in this edition 2017 by Wrecking Ball Press.

Copyright Will Self

Design by humandesign.co.uk

WRECKING BALL PRESS

How was your day? he'd say, at Broadway Lodge, in the somnolent suburbs of Weston-Super-Mare, in the mid-1980s. How was your day? He wore khaki cargo pants – although they weren't called that yet – and had a nice line in the homiletic: Try and get up from that chair, he'd say – and when I expressed perplexity, continued: Trying is lying – either you get up or you don't, and it's the same with your addiction... On another occasion, when I accused him and his fellow counsellors of brainwashing us, he was unrepentant: We have to wash your brain, Will... he angled his cleanly-shaven chin at me, adamant: because it's dirty... To purge our dirty brains, we had to write out our sins on ruled paper, in Biro. The exercise called for examples of our powerlessness and the damage it had caused. Literary affectations were not appreciated – style was anathema. Drunk driving and sexual ravishing – bad faith and theft, the florid hysteria of pathological intoxication – my peccadilloes had sutured day to night, then torn out the stitches... How was your day? My girlfriend came on Sunday with the other visitors, and we had sex in a flowerbed in the grounds. Both of us were anorexic – but the loam was soft and the waxy rhododendron leaves an effective screen. Even so, the habit of confession was already moulding me, and when he asked about my day, I told him – and so was put on report. Coming off methadone, I slid sweaty from under institutional candlewick, and went downstairs to sit up with the night watchman – a solid presence in shirt, tie and spectacles. We smoked – that being the way of it back then – quite unashamed, and for hour upon hour I watched his spectral reflection in the un-curtained windows of the patients' lounge. Out there, in the deeply suburban and profoundly provincial darkness, the masses dreamt of sex and death. How was your day..? My father came, and I was released into his charge – we went for lunch at the Atlantic Hotel on the seafront, and ate slices of sad tan beef, sliced on a mobile carvery by an ancient waiter. Silver service, indeed – the wings of flustered gulls were caught by the carvery's shiny and retinal cover, their costive cries – Sheeeeit! Sheeeeit! – came down to us from a local void, while my father sat, implacable, a worsted rock. I said, you were an adult before the war, things must've been so different then – the very quality of daily life... You have to tell me about it – you have to convey it to me... I understand what you're asking, he replied, but I have regretfully to inform you, I'm not the man for the job... He took a swig from his glass tankard full of pissy bitter ...You see, while I may have lived for a long time, so far as I'm concerned, it's always been... now. He sets down the tankard, sits back, gasps. Burps. I thought then – think now, again, of my philosophy tutor at university, an elegant young man – then – who later fell victim to severe depression. A mutual friend told me, the philosopher had followed an ambulance's siren call to the local hospital and asked to be committed. When he'd taught me, he'd already been interested in the provisional nature of the thinking I – and later on he developed a comprehensive philosophy of the episodic self. For him, the human subject is but a mayfly, born for a day... For him, each morning awakening is a true renaissance, of necessity accompanied by our recovery of this classical learning: the record of our former days we call... our memory. For him, the notion that our lives constitute a narrative, written into being by our enduring and indissoluble selves is worse than naïve – it's pernicious, encouraging in us all sorts of monstrous delusions... How was your day..? Yeah, how was it, you savage and world-despoiling ape, sitting in your tree, scratching your balls in the shadow of the mushroom cloud you just farted..? At night I sat in my oak-panelled room, underlining numbered propositions in Biro, injecting amphetamine sulphate, in solution, under the smooth skin of my boyish belly – the subcutaneous stitches hemming the hurting dawn. Recent brain research – surely, the only sort that matters – has much to tell us about the most savage and successful production we mount in our mind-theatres: pain. In the abandoned dead-end corridors and rubbish-strewn airing courts of our derelict memory palaces there remain only the faint echoes of the blows that were struck, and the echoes of our dying screams... We recall only the peak of pain – not its duration, only its point break – not the long fetch of our dying days, day upon day, one washing over the other, across the sea-slick sands of lost time... I've never kept a diary – or at least, not an ordinal one, which is surely the only sort that counts... To do so seemed inimical to the kind of writer I wanted to be: one who, whatever his waywardness, heeded his teachers' advice. When I left Broadway Lodge I prevailed upon the Director of Treatment, a big-headed man called Ed, to show me the notes my counsellor had made about me. The brainwasher's comments turned out to be terse physical observations: He has washed his hair today... and shaved... Doesn't appear to have showered today – his clothes are dirty... So far as my addiction counsellor was concerned, godliness wasn't just close to cleanliness, but synonymous. How right he was: three decades later, as I sit down to write a memoir of those desperate days, the same bitter bile repeats on me... because it's never a case of how was your day – only how is it? How is the endless day of the mayfly you always are, the once and future king of Now..? Yes, that they came to be called cargo pants is evidence, surely, that they were cargo pants in waiting – and therefore always to be so welcomed. I cannot be interred in the soft loam of the simple past, I refuse the easy certainties of a fictionalised life. Nietzsche claims that memory always yields to pride – but these aren't memories, which, taken in sum, amount to a personal history. No, no, you dirty-brained boy, forever trying to rise from your writing chair – they're daymares from which I now know, you'll never awake...

London, September 2017

# HOW

# WAS

# YOUR

# DAY